VROMAN'S
PASADENA

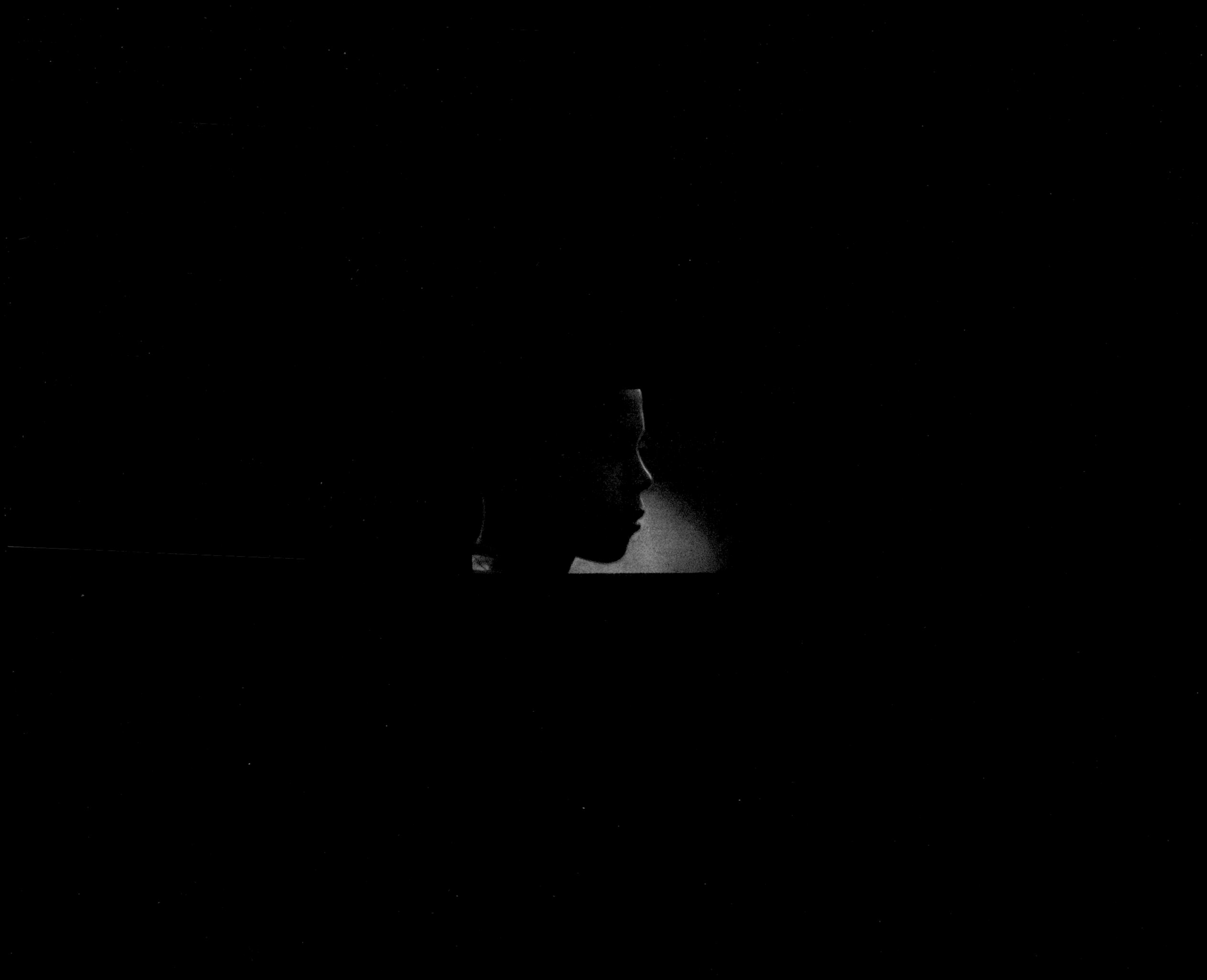

And I Must Hurry for the Sea is Coming In . . .

by George Mendoza

photographs by DeWayne Dalrymple

design by Herb Lubalin

Prentice-Hall, Inc. ENGLEWOOD CLIFFS, N.J.

Jean Reynolds . . . who makes impossible dreams come true.

And I Must Hurry for the Sea is Coming In . . .

BY GEORGE MENDOZA
PHOTOGRAPHS BY DEWAYNE DALRYMPLE

LIBRARY OF CONGRESS CATALOG NUMBER: 76-75382

J

13-036517-3

When I am a man, then I shall be a hunter

When I am a man, then I shall be a harpooner

When I am a man, then I shall be a canoe-builder

When I am a man, then I shall be a carpenter

When I am a man, then I shall be an artisan

Oh father! ya ha ha ha

KWAKIUTL INDIAN

And I must hurry for the sea is coming in…

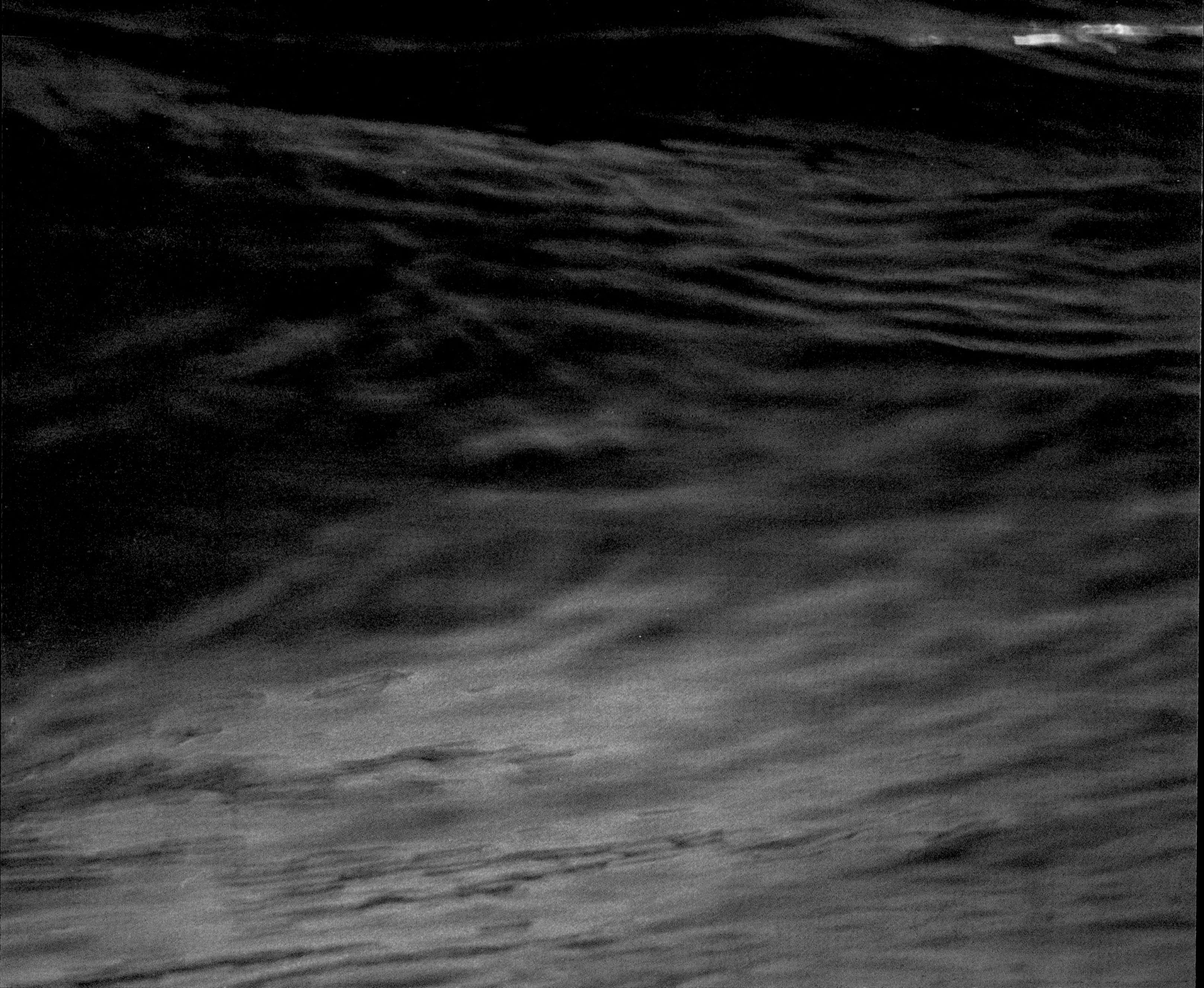

the sea is coming in

though wind and sea are set against me

I will take my boat

INTREPID

And I will go into the dawn wind

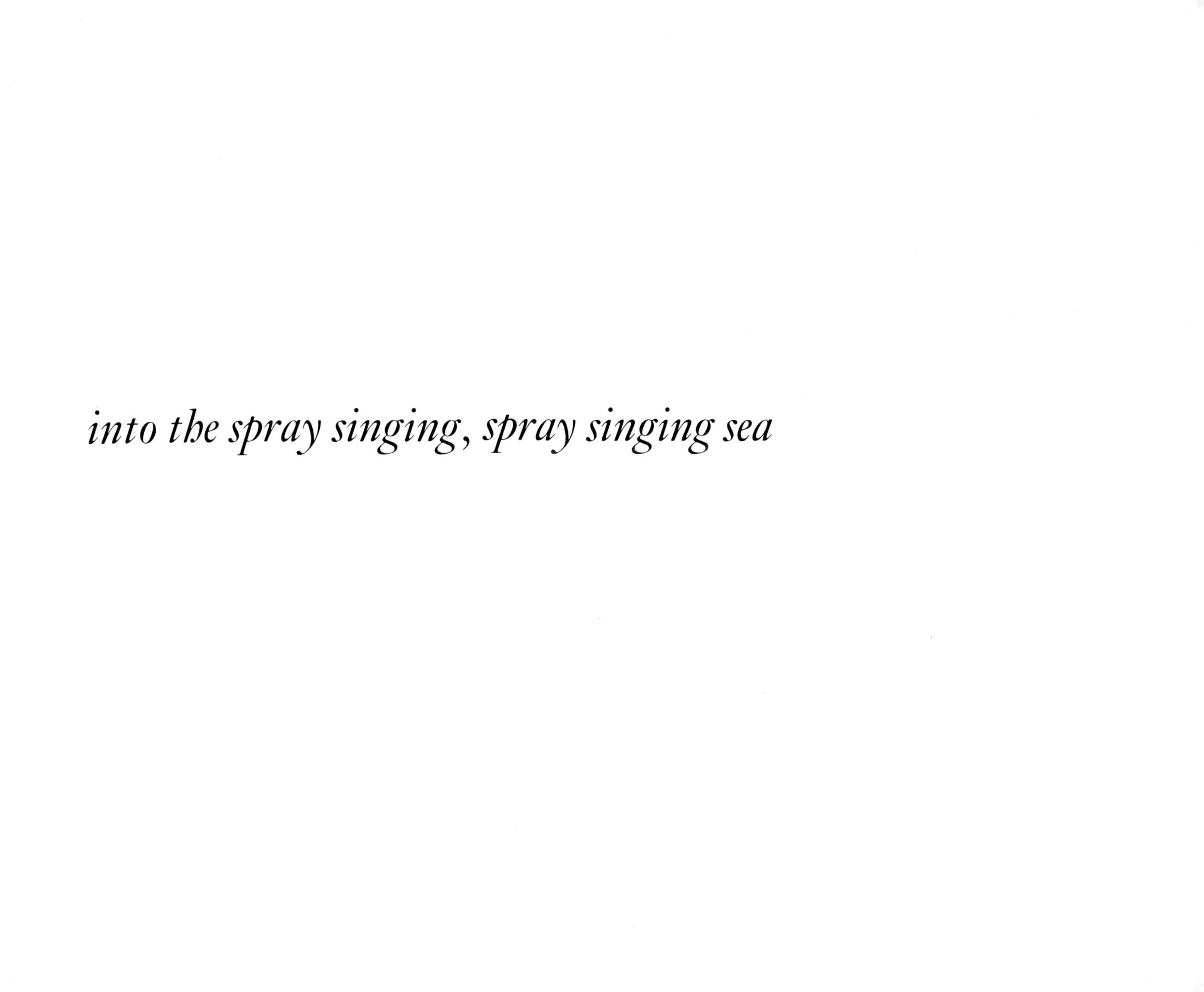

into the spray singing, spray singing sea

and set a sail on the tip of a star

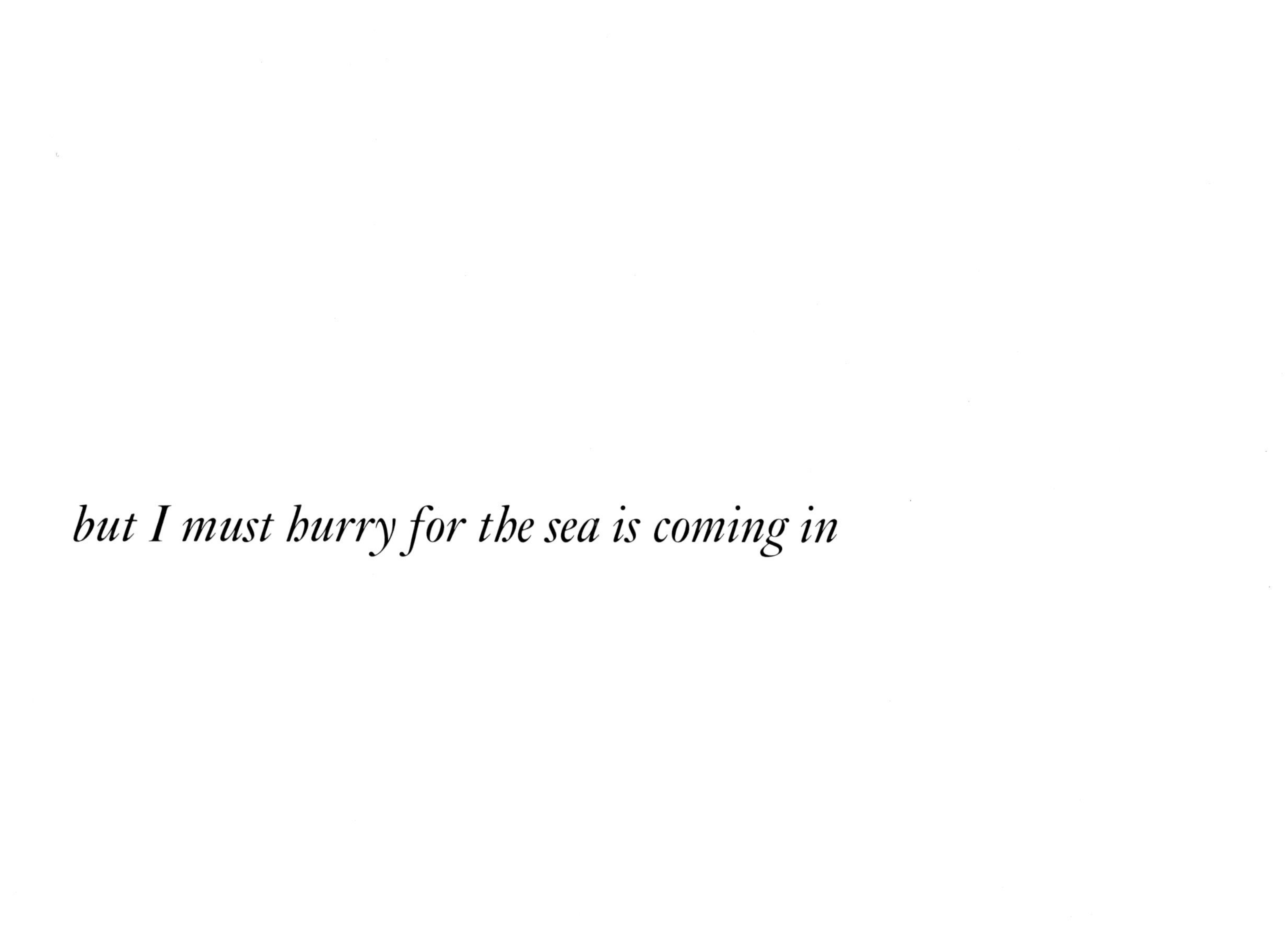

but I must hurry for the sea is coming in

It will not break me

Oh father, it will not break me

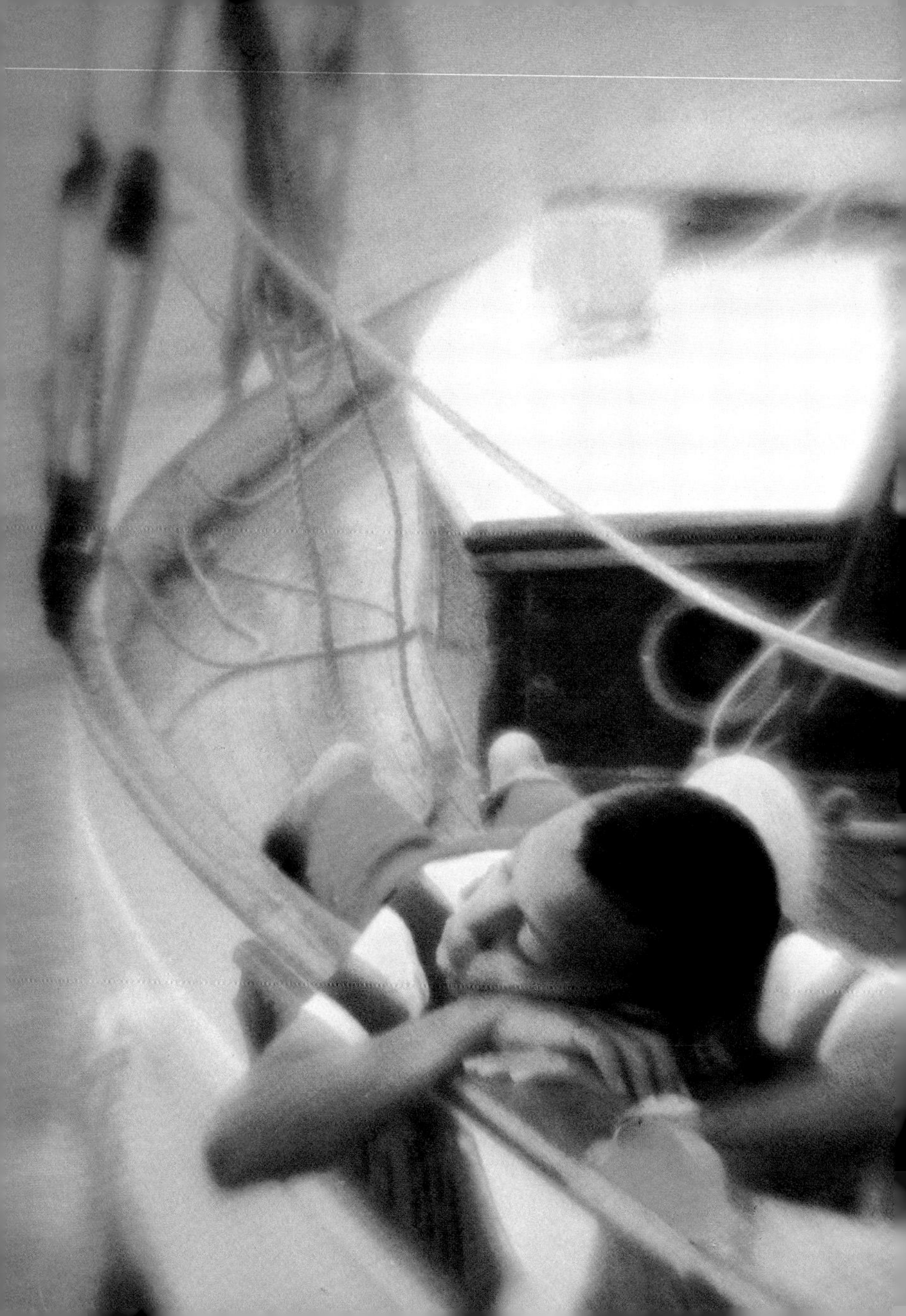

I must hurry for the sea is coming in…

the sea is coming in

the sea is coming in . . .

George Mendoza, poet-allegorist, winner of the 1968 Lewis Carroll Shelf Award for The Hunter I Might Have Been, searches for meaning in a world scorched with hate. Mendoza's unique talent in the range of allegory and poetry has been demonstrated in his impressive list of recent works: Allegory: And Amedeo Asked, How Does One Become a Man?, The Puma and the Pearl, A Piece of String, The Caterpillar Man, Flowers and Grasses and Weeds. Novel: The Hawk is Humming. Poetry: The Sand Poems, The Hunter I Might Have Been, The Starfish Trilogy, Fish in the Sky. Fables and tall tales for all ages: The Gillygoofang, Gwot! Horribly funny hairticklers, The Crack in the Wall, A Wart Snake in a Fig Tree, The Practical Man.

DeWayne Dalrymple's impressionistic pictures delve into the emotional depths of the subconscious. A creative and interpretative photographer, Dalrymple distinguished himself with his sensitive, unforgettable illustrations for The Hunter I Might Have Been.

In 1962, Herb Lubalin received the highest recognition for his achievements as a graphic designer. "The Art Director of the Year Award" was presented to him by The National Society of Art Directors. He has recently turned his talents towards publishing and is credited with the design of such award-winning books as "Portal to America — The Lower East Side", "Castro's Cuba, Cuba's Fidel" and "Harlem On My Mind."